SECRETS

also by Jessie Orton Jones

and Elizabeth Orton Jones

SMALL RAIN

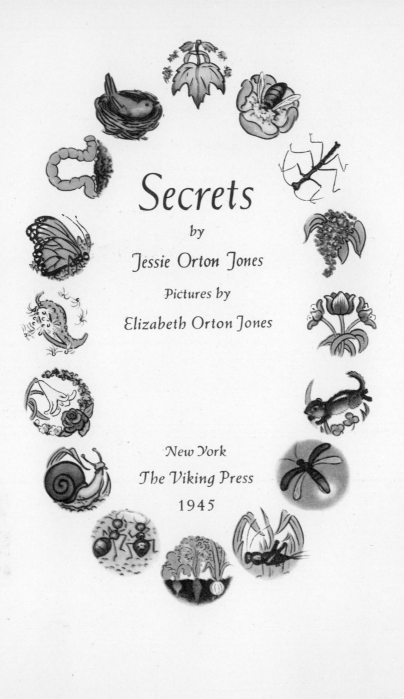

Secrets

by

Jessie Orton Jones

Pictures by

Elizabeth Orton Jones

New York

The Viking Press

1945

Copyright 1945 by Jessie Orton Jones and Elizabeth Orton Jones
First published by the Viking Press in August 1945
Published on the same day in the dominion of Canada by
The Macmillan Company of Canada Limited

Second Printing October 1945

Printed in the United States of America
By National Process Company

Like the green leaves we do not see in wintertime,
Like the bare trees we do not see in summertime,
That is the way with Spirit—God.

——JULIE

To Julie — my friend

I

Have you ever waked up in the middle of the night,
    And stayed awake a little while to think?
        I have.
    It is such a happy time,
    With nothing to hear, nothing to see,
    And nobody there but God and me.
    When I go to sleep again,
I know something that I never knew before.

When morning comes shining round my curtain
    I feel quite new inside.
The things in my room seem that way too—
My dear shoes that have waited for me all night long,
    I push my feet into them,
    Jump into my clothes,
And, skipping through the house and down the stairs,
    I run outdoors.

Outdoors is always fresh and new
    In morning-time.
It has been washed in dewdrops
    In the night.
That makes our grass look like a silver carpet,
With jewels sparkling all over it.
I like to roll downhill on this soft carpet,
    And wash my face in dew,
    And laugh and laugh.
When I get to the bottom of the hill,
And lie there, dizzy, with my hair all wet,
    I look up to the sky,
    And laugh some more.

III

The sun shines through our trees in long white rays.
    I see a million tiny specks in them.
Sometimes I try to catch them in my hands,
    But I never can.
    I used to call them fairies.
    Now I think they're angels,
    Sliding down the sunbeams
    To find me.

The warm sun is shining on our garden.
That's where I planted seeds not long ago.
    Such little wrinkled things they were
    As I held them in my hand!
Now they have grown into vegetables,
Many shapes, many colors, many tastes.
How could each seed grow into the right vegetable
    And nothing else—
The red radish, the white onion, the yellow carrot,
    All down there together
    In the same black earth?
How could they know just how to be themselves?
God must have whispered to them in the ground
And told each one the secret of itself.

Sometimes I hear God's whisper in the night.
The birds do, too, because they answer him
    In small bird voices.
I think he's telling them just what to do.
I think he tells them how to build their nests,
    And make them safe for eggs.
He tells them how to feed the baby birds.
He tells them when to fly away from cold,
And where to find a warmer place to live.
    So many things for birds to know!
    So many things to do!

Flowers always know what they should do.
The buttercup grows always shining yellow
    And the larkspur blue.
The lily always smells like lily,
    And the rose like rose.
Do you suppose the yellow buttercup
    Would like to be a rose?
Or the rose have the perfume of a lily?
    I think each one looks happy
    Being its very own self!

We have tulips in our flower bed.
This spring they looked so pretty—pink and white.
Now they've gone to sleep in small brown bulbs.
Next spring they'll bloom again—still pink and white.
All winter God remembers who they are,
And never gets them mixed with other things.
I'm sure he'll always know that I am me.

VIII

I am glad I'm who I am;
I like to be myself.
Even when I do the wrong thing,
I know I am the right person.

I can climb our apple tree,
If I put my feet carefully in the right places,
    And pull myself up by my hands.
Then I come to my little seat in the arms of the tree.
    I can sit there and see everything.
I can see a measuring worm, light green,
    Climbing our apple tree.
    At every step
He has to make his whole body into a hump,
While his back feet catch up with his front feet.
That is a hard way to climb a tree,
    But it's his way
    And he doesn't seem to mind.

Do you like secrets?
There is one between bees and apple blossoms.
Bees need honey for their babies—
Apple blossoms need bees to help make apples.
So they dress themselves all up in pink petals
    For the bees to see,
And make a little feast of honey in their hearts.
    Then the bees come buzzing,
And push their noses deep into the sweetness,
And shake the yellow pollen all around,
    And wipe their feet and go.
The secret between bees and apple blossoms is
      like that.
    I am in the secret too,
When I have apple sauce and honey for my supper.

The lilac bush has no fruit at all.
It seems to grow just to be beautiful.
The lilac flowers are bending over now,
Looking in the mirror of the bird bath.
    I can see them there,
With ripples in the water wrinkling them.
      God must have smiled
      When he made lilacs!

Did you ever have a chipmunk for a friend?
    I have one that I call "Chippy."
Sometimes he comes right on my lap,
    If I put bread there,
    And stay very still.
    Then he sits up,
And holds the bread in his thin brown fingers,
Turning it over and over as he eats,
And watching me with his round, bright eye,
And listening with his tiny ears.
    If I even so much as breathe,
He stuffs the bread in his cheek and scampers off.

Have you seen that strange insect called "walking-
    stick"?
That is just what he looks like—a walking stick.
Isn't he funny? I think he is one of God's little jokes!

I like to hear the cricket in the grass.
I think he has a cozy little song,
That sounds quite nice sometimes inside the house.
His song will bring his dearest friend to him;
    But he must sing the song
    And she must hear it.

Do you know what tree I love best?
    I love our maple.
    It is always first in everything—
First in spring to get its scarlet blossoms,
First to grow its little pinkish leaves,
First in fall to put on golden colors.
Then it looks the loveliest of all—
    Like sunshine,
    Like clouds.
Oh, sometimes I throw my arms
    Around our maple!

I used to think our trees all died in winter,
    Because I saw they hadn't any leaves,
But now I know that they are only sleeping—
    Resting from their long summer's work.
    Maybe under their snow blanket,
They are dreaming of blossoms and leaves
    For another spring.

The milkweed seeds need to go far away for planting,
So they have white fluff-balls to carry them along.
    High they go,
        Floating through the air,
To find just the place for milkweeds to grow.

XVIII

A butterfly will find the milkweed plant,
    Wherever it is growing—
    A mother butterfly,
    With eggs to lay.
The tender leaves are good food for her babies.
They will eat, and grow, and grow some more,
    And change—
        And change again,
Into beautiful new butterflies,
    To fill the air.

Ants are the busiest people I know,
Always running up and running down,
Perhaps because they make their doors in hilltops.
They have so many loads to carry up,
And just as many more to carry down,
And always seem to be in such a hurry!
They work so hard to keep things tidy,
I'm sure they love their little homes in hills.

This little fellow must love his home
    Because he never leaves it.
    I have to laugh
When I see him hunching down the garden path
    With his house on his back!
    God knew he had a soft body
    And didn't want him to get hurt,
So he gave him a shell for a house.

How could God think of so many kinds of houses?
There are millions of houses that I can't even see.
There must be lots of very funny ones!
　　Mole houses—
　　　　Frog houses—
　　　　　　Beaver houses—
　　　　　Stork nests on chimneys,
　　　　　Squirrel nests in trees.
　　　　Houses for everyone!
　　　　And my house
　　　　　For me.

When evening brings darkness to our garden,
All the flowers fold up and go to sleep.
But fireflies just begin to waken
And turn their tiny flashlights on and off.
Sometimes I catch one of them in my hand
And use him for a candle up to bed.

XXIII

The sun has gone to other lands,
    To make a day out there;
But I shall never miss him,
    Because my moon is here.

At night I like to snuggle in my pillow,
    And close my eyes up tight.
Then I can see pictures in my mind—
I can see vegetables growing in the sun,
And butterflies and birds up in the sky.
I can see the light green worm climbing our apple tree.
I can see all the things in our garden.

They were so busy all day long,
They never noticed once that I was there—
Except for little Chip, who likes my bread.
But they are all my friends
    Because I know them.
I know the tastes of fruits and vegetables,
I feel the morning dew on my bare feet,
And hear the cricket chirping in the grass.
    I know the secret of each one of them.

God gives me love to love the world he made.
    I fold it all up close inside myself,
    And say a little thank you in my prayer.